C000193173

Brave

A Cherrytree Book

Designed and produced by
A S Publishing

First published 1993
by Cherrytree Press Ltd
Windsor Bridge Road
Bath, Avon BA2 3AX

Copyright © Cherrytree Press Ltd 1993

British Library Cataloguing in Publication Data
Amos, Janine
  Brave. – (Feelings Series)
  I. Title II. Green, Gwen III. Series
  152.4

ISBN 0-7451-5194-9

Printed and bound in Spain by Graficas Reunidas, S.A.

All rights reserved. No part of this publication may be
reproduced, stored in a retrieval system or transmitted, in
any form or by any means without the prior permission in
writing of the publisher, nor be otherwise circulated in any
form of binding or cover other than that in which it is
published and without a similar condition including this
condition being imposed on the subsequent purchaser.

Brave

By Janine Amos

Illustrated by Gwen Green

CHERRYTREE BOOKS

Dean's story

Dean was staying at his grandad's. They'd been listening to an adventure story on the radio. But the programme had finished. Now Dean's grandad was fast asleep.

Dean went into the front room. It was Dean's favourite place in the house. The room was full of special things. There were old books on dusty shelves. There was a book of stamps from all over the world, and a coin collection. But most of all, Dean liked looking at his grandad's pocket watches. Some were more than a hundred years old! One had belonged to his grandad's grandad.

Dean climbed on to a chair. He carefully lifted down a wooden box. Inside were six shiny watches, all ticking loudly.

Dean looked at the watches for a long time. He wasn't supposed to touch them without his grandad. But Dean wanted to very much.

"Just this once," he thought, as he slowly picked one up.

Dean knew a lot about the watch. He knew that if he pressed a tiny button the lid would pop up. Then you could see the workings inside. Dean wanted to press that button. "Just this once," he thought.

Then the pocket watch slipped. It fell out of Dean's hands, against a chair, and on to the floor.

What would you do now if you were Dean?

Dean picked up the watch and turned it over. Across the glass was a long crack! Dean's heart was beating fast. He slipped the watch back into the box with the others. He stood on the chair and placed the box back on the shelf. Dean could hear his grandad snoring in the other room. "If I don't tell him, he'll never know it was me," thought Dean.

At teatime Dean wasn't hungry. He kept thinking about the broken watch. He felt a bit sick. "It's not fair to keep it a secret," thought Dean. Dean wanted to tell his grandad what he'd done. But he was scared. "I'll tell him at bedtime," thought Dean.

All evening Dean was very quiet. At last his grandad asked him to get ready for bed. Dean took a deep breath. Slowly he told his grandad everything.

How do you think Dean feels? How does his grandad feel?

Dean's grandad listened until Dean had finished. He didn't say a word. Then he went into the front room and Dean followed him. Dean's grandad lifted down the wooden box. He took out the broken watch.

"This watch has been perfect for one hundred and twenty years," said Dean's grandad. "And you've broken it in five minutes."

"I'm sorry," said Dean quietly.

"Go to bed," said his grandad.

Dean was crying as he climbed into bed. He knew how cross his grandad was. Dean wished that he wasn't staying the night at grandad's. He wished that he could go home.

After a while, Dean heard his grandad coming.
"Are you still awake?" asked Dean's grandad. "I've brought you some hot milk." Dean's grandad sat down on the bed. "It's only the glass that's broken," he said. "I think we can get that watch mended."

Dean started to sip his milk.

"You were very brave to tell me," his grandad went on. "It's hard to own up. When I was your age, I smashed a window. I worried for two days before I told my father."

"And what did he say?" Dean wanted to know.

"He said that he knew already!" Dean's grandad laughed. "He said that he was waiting."

"Waiting for what?" asked Dean.

"To see how brave I was," said Dean's grandad.

How do you think Dean feels now?

Feeling like Dean

Have you ever felt like Dean? Have you ever broken something that didn't belong to you? Were you brave enough to own up and say sorry?

Special things

Everyone has special things which they like to take care of. If those things get lost or broken, people can become upset. They may get angry at first, like Dean's grandad. But they don't stay upset for ever.

Scared to say sorry

Dean made a mistake. He shouldn't have touched his grandad's watch. Everyone makes mistakes sometimes. When you've made a mistake, it's often hard to talk about it. You want to say sorry – it's only fair. But you're scared of being told off. That's why you need to be brave.

Growing up

Being brave is about doing something you don't much like. It's about facing up to fear or danger or pain. Everyone needs to be brave sometimes. It's part of growing up. Read the stories in this book. Think about the people in the stories. When was the last time you were brave?

Clare's story

Clare was in bed but she couldn't sleep. She could hear her dad shouting in the other room. And she could hear her mum shouting too. They were having a row.

"Not again, please," thought Clare. "Please make them be friends." The shouting went on. Clare wanted to ask her mum and dad to stop. But she was too scared. They'd only tell her to go back to bed, anyway. Clare felt frightened. Her mum and dad were always cross with each other these days. What was going on? Clare pulled her pillow around her ears. She tried to hum a song. If she hummed loud enough she couldn't hear the shouting. After a while Clare fell asleep.

When she came home from school the next day Clare had a surprise.

"Is that you, Clare?" called a voice from the kitchen.

"Aunty Fran! Yippee!" called Clare. Aunty Fran was her mum's best friend. She was one of Clare's favourite people.

Clare ran into the kitchen. Aunty Fran gave Clare a kiss. Clare's mum was there too. Her face was all red. Clare could tell that she'd been crying.

"Can I show you my new bike?" Clare asked Aunty Fran.

"In a little while," Aunty Fran told her. "At the moment your mum and I are talking."

How do you think Clare feels? Have you ever felt like this?

Clare went to her bedroom. She wondered why her mum was crying. There were lots of things that Clare wanted to know.

Just then there was a knock at the door. It was Aunty Fran.

"And how are you, Clare?" asked Aunty Fran.

Suddenly Clare wanted to tell Aunty Fran everything. She didn't know how to start. "Mum and dad were rowing last night," she began. Soon Clare was telling Aunty Fran everything.

Do you think Aunty Fran can help?

"Do you find it scary?" asked Aunty Fran.

"Yes," said Clare. "They row all the time. Are they shouting about me? Have I done something wrong?" she asked.

Aunty Fran held Clare's hand.

"No," she said. "You've done nothing wrong. Your mum and dad love you very much."

"Then what is it?" Clare asked.

"Your mum and dad aren't happy together at the moment," said Aunty Fran. There was a long pause.

"Will they split up, like Jessica's parents?" asked Clare.

"I don't think so," said Aunty Fran carefully.

Then Aunty Fran asked Clare for some paper and a felt pen. She wrote down her telephone number in big pink letters.

"Now, whenever you feel worried or scared you're to let me know," said Aunty Fran. "We can talk about it."

Clare nodded. Aunty Fran put her arm around Clare. "Thank you for telling me, Clare," she said. "You've been brave. And I'm going to help you as much as I can."

"You've helped me today," said Clare.

"Good," said Aunty Fran. And she gave Clare a big hug. "Now let's see that new bike."

Feeling like Clare

Have you ever felt like Clare? Have you been upset by the way some adults behave? Grown-up behaviour can make you feel confused, frightened or unhappy. You might not understand it. It may help you to know that lots of children feel like this sometimes.

Talking about it

Clare found it hard to talk at first. But she was brave. She knew that Aunty Fran could help her. Talking about your worries is a good idea. Tell an adult you trust. They'll help by listening. They may be able to explain the things you don't understand. Who would you talk to if you felt like Clare?

Linda's story

"Take your hand away. Let me see the cut!" said Linda's mum.

Linda moved her hand from her eye. Her fingers were covered in blood. She started to shake. Linda's mum pressed a cloth hard against the cut.

"I'm trying to stop the bleeding," she told Linda.

It seemed a long time before Linda's mum said anything else. When she did, she smiled. "We're lucky, Linda,' she said. "It's a deep cut but it's missed your eye."

Linda's mum taped a big piece of cottonwool to Linda's forehead. "Now I want you to wash your hands and wait here quietly," said Linda's mum. "I'll just go and wake Joe."

Joe was Linda's baby brother.

"Where are we going?" asked Linda.

"To the hospital," said Linda's mum.

Linda didn't like the sound of that.

Linda sat and waited. Her head ached a bit. Her mum was soon back with the baby.

"I don't want to go to the hospital," said Linda. She felt her heart beating fast.

Linda's mum bent down. She looked right into Linda's eyes. "You need some stitches," she said. "No arguments. O.K?"

"O.K." said Linda.

"That's a brave girl," said Linda's mum.

Why is Linda brave?

The hospital was busy. Linda held her mum's hand. Soon a nurse came over and wrote down Linda's name. Gently she lifted up the plaster and looked at Linda's cut.

"Ouch!" said the nurse. "You'll need the doctor to put a few stitches in that. How did it happen?"

"Someone threw a pebble," said Linda.

Linda, her mum and Joe waited for the doctor. It got very hot in the waiting room. More and more people came. A baby started to cry. Joe woke up and he joined in.

"What are stitches for?" Linda asked.

"They'll help your cut to heal," said her mum.

"I'd rather go home," said Linda.

"I know you would," said her mum. "But I promise that I'll stay with you all the time."

Why does Linda want to go home?

After a long time the nurse came back.

"Dr Stone will see you now," she said to Linda. Linda gulped. She wanted to run away.

The nurse took hold of Linda's hand. Linda grabbed at her mum's skirt. All linked together, they walked into the doctor's room. When Dr Stone saw them he smiled.

"Don't look so scared. I'm not going to eat you!" he said.

Dr Stone helped Linda to get up on to the small bed. Linda's mum sat down in the corner of the room. Linda was very cold. Her throat was dry.

"Now I'm going to tell you exactly what I'm doing, Linda," said Dr Stone. "It will hurt a bit – but only for a minute."

"O.K." said Linda in a small voice.

How is Linda feeling at this moment?

Dr Stone told Linda that he would freeze her cut with an injection. "Then you won't feel any pain afterwards," he said. Linda felt the injection go into her forehead. But Dr Stone was talking to her all the time.

"That's the worst part over," he said. Then he explained how he would pull the cut together with stitches. Linda was lying very still. She looked up at the doctor. He gave her a big wink.

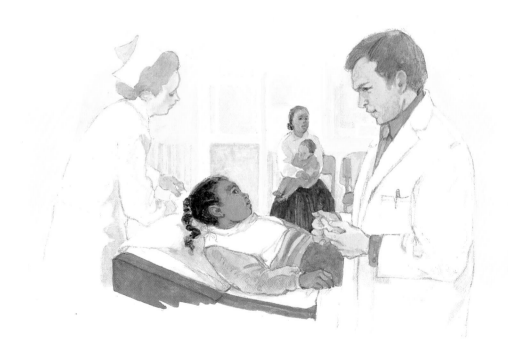

Soon the doctor had finished. "All over for today!" he said.

Linda sat up carefully.

"You'll have to come back next week to have those stitches out," said Dr Stone. "But that won't worry you because you've been so brave already!"

Then Dr Stone gave Linda a present. It was a sticky badge.

"Do you know what it says?" asked Dr Stone.

Linda read the words. "I WAS BRAVE
AT THE HOSPITAL TODAY," she said, smiling.

How did Dr Stone help Linda?

Feeling like Linda

Linda was brave in two ways. She was brave about going to hospital. And she was brave about having the stitches. Linda had some help, too. Her mum helped by staying with her. And Dr Stone helped by explaining what was going on.

The scary times

Think about the stories in this book. Dean, Clare and Linda were each brave in different ways. They had to face up to things they didn't much like. They had to cope with the scary times in life.

Being brave

Life is full of scary times. You have to go on being brave – even when you're grown up. But other people can help you. They can help by explaining things or by listening. They can help just by being there.

Feeling strong

Being brave is hard at the time. But afterwards you feel strong. You've learnt something new. Remember this the next time you need to be brave.

If you are feeling frightened or unhappy, don't keep it to yourself. Talk to an adult you can trust, like a parent or a teacher. If you feel really alone, you could telephone or write to one of these offices. Remember, there is always someone who can help.

Childline
Freephone 0800 1111
Address: Freepost 1111, London   N1 0BR

NSPCC Child Protection Line
Freephone 0800 800500

NCH Careline
Birmingham (021) 440 5970
Cardiff (0222) 229461
Glasgow (041) 221 6722
Glenrothes (0592) 759651
Leeds (0532) 456456
London (081) 514 1177
Luton (0582) 422751
Maidstone (0622) 56677
Preston (0772) 24006

NAYPIC
Especially for children who are in care
(061) 953 4051

The Samaritans
Dial 100 – The operator will put you through.